HARRIET POPHAM

GREAT BRITISH
FLOWER SHOW

A HORTICULTURAL COLOURING
ADVENTURE

HarperCollins*Publishers*
1 London Bridge Street
London SE1 9GF

www.harpercollins.co.uk

First published by HarperCollins*Publishers* 2016

3 5 7 9 10 8 6 4 2

Illustrations © Harriet Popham 2016

A catalogue record of this book is
available from the British Library

ISBN 978-0-00-818234-2

Printed and bound in Spain by Graficas Estella, Spain

MIX
Paper from
responsible sources
FSC C007454

FSC™ is a non-profit international organisation established to promote
the responsible management of the world's forests. Products carrying the
FSC label are independently certified to assure consumers that they come
from forests that are managed to meet the social, economic and
ecological needs of present and future generations,
and other controlled sources.

Find out more about HarperCollins and the environment at
www.harpercollins.co.uk/green

HARRIET POPHAM

GREAT BRITISH

FLOWER SHOW

A HORTICULTURAL COLOURING
ADVENTURE

HarperCollins*Publishers*

For Granny and Grandad

Flowers have always featured in my life. My grandparents' garden was bursting with beds of begonias, tubs of tulips and hedges of honeysuckle. They delighted in tending this paradise well into their nineties, and their sitting-room walls were covered in certificates won at local flower shows over the years. My grandmother loved to sit in the garden with the sun on her face and to imitate the bird song, and it's for this reason that you'll find some little feathered friends in my drawings too!

I've filled this book with as many flowers as I could possibly dream of, from blooms spilling out of wellies and watering cans to dazzling flower show tables and stately home shrubberies. Whether it's an intricately detailed garden scene or a bold, up-close botanical painting, all of these drawings are designed to bring you plenty of enjoyment and space to add your own creativity.

So, whether you decide to embellish a bouquet or add hues to the hydrangeas, lose yourself in the pleasure of colouring and watch your garden grow!

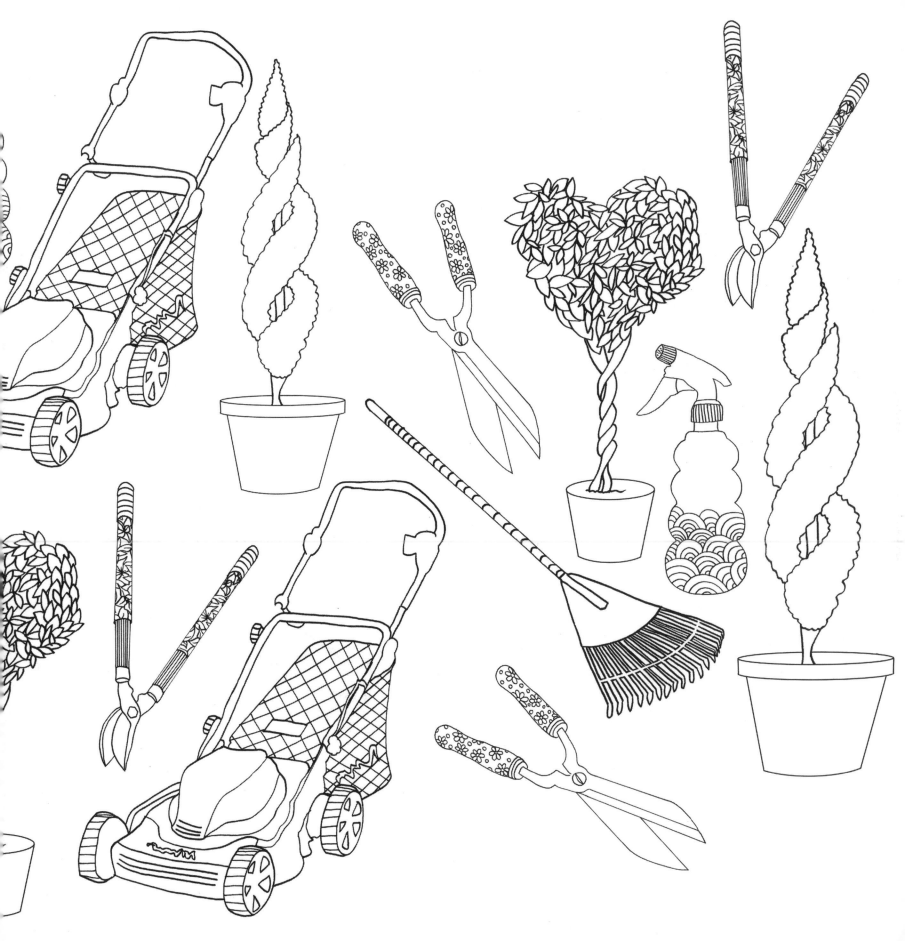

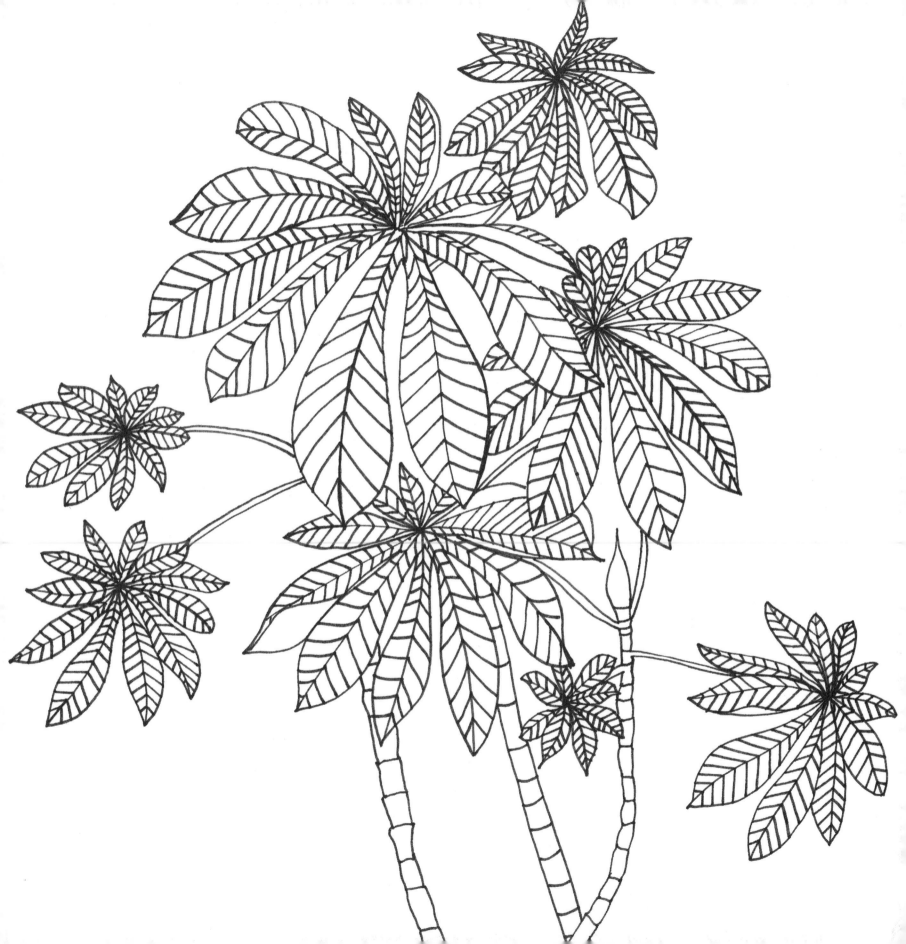

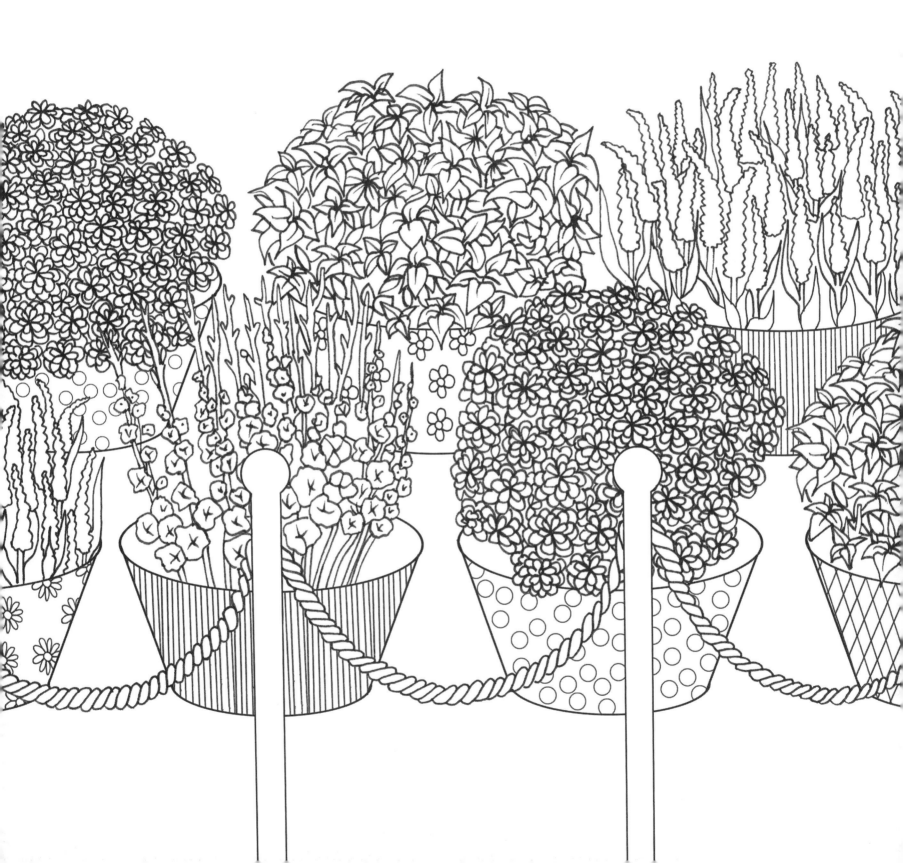

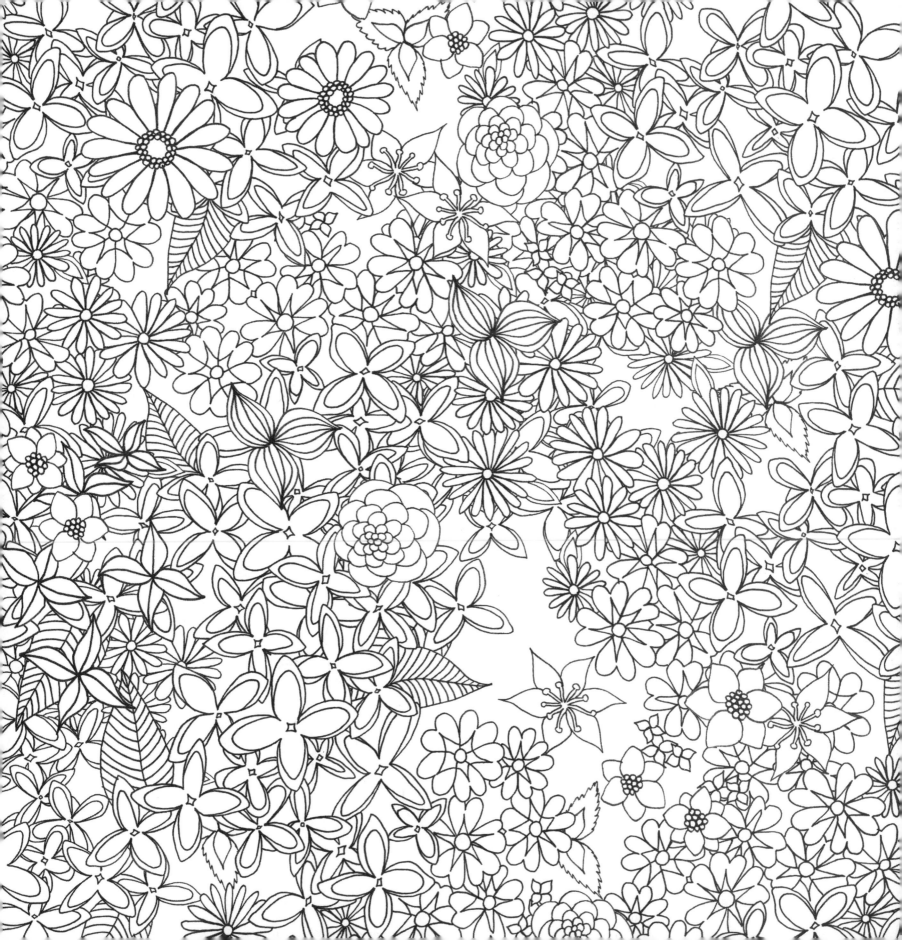

Create your own flower show here ...